MAD LIBS®

GRADUATION MAD LIBS

concept created by Roger Price and Leonard Stern

SCHOLASTIC

ISBN 978-0-545-87488-5

Mad Libs format and text copyright © 2005 by Price Stern Sloan, an imprint of Penguin Random House LLC. All rights reserved. Published by Scholastic Inc., 557 Broadway, New York, NY 10012, by arrangement with Price Stern Sloan, an imprint of Penguin Young Readers Group, a division of Penguin Random House LLC. *MAD LIBS* is a registered trademark of Penguin Random House LLC. SCHOLASTIC and associated logos are trademarks and/or registered trademarks of Scholastic Inc.

12 11 10 9 8 7 6 5   21/0

INSTRUCTIONS

MAD LIBS® is a game for people who don't like games!
It can be played by one, two, three, four, or forty.

• RIDICULOUSLY SIMPLE DIRECTIONS

In this tablet you will find stories containing blank spaces where words are left out. One player, the READER, selects one of these stories. The READER does not tell anyone what the story is about. Instead, he/she asks the other players, the WRITERS, to give him/her words. These words are used to fill in the blank spaces in the story.

• TO PLAY

The READER asks each WRITER in turn to call out a word—an adjective or a noun or whatever the space calls for—and uses them to fill in the blank spaces in the story. The result is a MAD LIBS® game.

When the READER then reads the completed MAD LIBS® game to the other players, they will discover that they have written a story that is fantastic, screamingly funny, shocking, silly, crazy, or just plain dumb—depending upon which words each WRITER called out.

• EXAMPLE (*Before* and *After*)

"_____!" he said _____
      EXCLAMATION   ADVERB

as he jumped into his convertible _____ and
                                       NOUN

drove off with his _____ wife.
                        ADJECTIVE

"*Ouch!*_____!" he said *stupidly*_____
      EXCLAMATION   ADVERB

as he jumped into his convertible *cat*_____ and
                                         NOUN

drove off with his *brave*_____ wife.
                        ADJECTIVE

QUICK REVIEW

In case you have forgotten what adjectives, adverbs, nouns, and verbs are, here is a quick review:

An **ADJECTIVE** describes something or somebody. *Lumpy, soft, ugly, messy,* and *short* are adjectives.

An **ADVERB** tells how something is done. It modifies a verb and usually ends in "ly." *Modestly, stupidly, greedily,* and *carefully* are adverbs.

A **NOUN** is the name of a person, place, or thing. *Sidewalk, umbrella, bridle, bathtub,* and *nose* are nouns.

A **VERB** is an action word. *Run, pitch, jump,* and *swim* are verbs. Put the verbs in past tense if the directions say PAST TENSE. *Ran, pitched, jumped,* and *swam* are verbs in the past tense.

When we ask for **A PLACE**, we mean any sort of place: a country or city *(Spain, Cleveland)* or a room *(bathroom, kitchen).*

An **EXCLAMATION** or **SILLY WORD** is any sort of funny sound, gasp, grunt, or outcry, like *Wow!, Ouch!, Whomp!, Ick!,* and *Gadzooks!*

When we ask for specific words, like a **NUMBER**, a **COLOR**, an **ANIMAL**, or a **PART OF THE BODY**, we mean a word that is one of those things, like *seven, blue, horse,* or *head*.

When we ask for a **PLURAL**, it means more than one. For example, *cat* pluralized is *cats*.

MAD LIBS® is fun to play with friends, but you can also play it by yourself! To begin with, DO NOT look at the story on the page below. Fill in the blanks on this page with the words called for. Then, using the words you have selected, fill in the blank spaces in the story.

Now you've created your own hilarious MAD LIBS® game!

FINAL EXAMS

ADJECTIVE _____

NUMBER _____

VERB _____

NUMBER _____

VERB _____

NOUN _____

OCCUPATION _____

VERB _____

PLURAL NOUN _____

TYPE OF SPORT _____

VERB _____

ROOM _____

VERB _____

PERSON IN ROOM (FEMALE)_____

A PLACE _____

NUMBER _____

VERB _____

ADVERB _____

FINAL EXAMS

I'm so nervous about taking my final exams! They're going to be so

_____! Can you believe that I have _____
      ADJECTIVE   NUMBER

of them? I'll have to _____ for _____ hours!
               VERB   NUMBER

I think I'll _____ my _____ exam, but I'm
           VERB   NOUN

afraid that my _____ exam will be really hard. My mom
              OCCUPATION

said that I have to _____ every night for the next few
                VERB

_____, which means that will be less time I have to
   PLURAL NOUN

play _____ and _____ on the phone. And
      TYPE OF SPORT   VERB

I doubt I'll have any time to clean my _____ or
                                     ROOM

_____ my laundry. My parents promised they would take
   VERB

me and my best friend _____ to _____
               PERSON IN ROOM (FEMALE)   A PLACE

if we both get at least a/an _____ on each of our exams.
                         NUMBER

So I'm going to _____ extra _____!
               VERB   ADVERB

MAD LIBS® is fun to play with friends, but you can also play it by yourself! To begin with, DO NOT look at the story on the page below. Fill in the blanks on this page with the words called for. Then, using the words you have selected, fill in the blank spaces in the story.

Now you've created your own hilarious MAD LIBS® game!

PARTY TIME!

ADJECTIVE_____

PLURAL NOUN _____

VERB ENDING IN "ING" _____

PLURAL NOUN _____

CELEBRITY (FEMALE) _____

PERSON IN ROOM (MALE)_____

SILLY WORD_____

VERB _____

TYPE OF FOOD (PLURAL) _____

NOUN _____

SAME TYPE OF FOOD (PLURAL)_____

ADJECTIVE_____

ADJECTIVE_____

TYPE OF SHOE (PLURAL) _____

SOMETHING ALIVE _____

NOUN _____

VERB ENDING IN "ING" _____

NOUN _____

SILLY WORD_____

PARTY TIME!

One of the most _____ things about graduating is that my
ADJECTIVE

_____ are _____ a huge party! I decided
PLURAL NOUN   VERB ENDING IN "ING"

to have a backyard barbecue for all of my family and _____.
PLURAL NOUN

I've invited my best friends _____, _____,
CELEBRITY (FEMALE)   PERSON IN ROOM (MALE)

and of course my teacher Mrs. _____. My dad is going
SILLY WORD

to _____ hamburgers and _____ on his
VERB   TYPE OF FOOD (PLURAL)

shiny new _____. He always thinks his _____
NOUN   SAME TYPE OF FOOD (PLURAL)

taste really _____, but I think they taste like _____
ADJECTIVE   ADJECTIVE

_____. My mom is going to make her famous
TYPE OF SHOE (PLURAL)

_____ salad, which is my favorite _____
SOMETHING ALIVE   NOUN

ever! Mom said after we finish _____, we can go
VERB ENDING IN "ING"

swimming in our new _____. _____!
NOUN   SILLY WORD

MAD LIBS® is fun to play with friends, but you can also play it by yourself! To begin with, DO NOT look at the story on the page below. Fill in the blanks on this page with the words called for. Then, using the words you have selected, fill in the blank spaces in the story.

Now you've created your own hilarious MAD LIBS® game!

GIFTS FOR THE GRAD

EXCLAMATION _____

ADJECTIVE _____

NUMBER _____

PLURAL NOUN _____

NOUN _____

VERB _____

A PLACE _____

PERSON IN ROOM (FEMALE) _____

NOUN _____

SOMETHING ALIVE _____

ADJECTIVE _____

NOUN _____

NOUN _____

A PLACE _____

NOUN _____

LANGUAGE _____

FOREIGN COUNTRY _____

ROOM _____

NOUN _____

VEHICLE _____

CELEBRITY (MALE) _____

COLOR _____

NUMBER _____

GIFTS FOR THE GRAD

_____! I got so many _____ graduation
     EXCLAMATION   ADJECTIVE

presents! I counted them and can you believe I have _____
                                                         NUMBER

presents in total? That's a lot of _____! My parents got
                                        PLURAL NOUN

me a brand-new _____ so that I can _____
                      NOUN   VERB

my homework when I get to _____. My grandma
                                 A PLACE

_____ bought me a beautiful _____
PERSON IN ROOM (FEMALE)   NOUN

shaped like a/an _____. It's _____! She said
                    SOMETHING ALIVE   ADJECTIVE

she had one just like it when she was a young _____.
                                                      NOUN

My little sister bought me a bright red _____. I can't
                                               NOUN

wait to wear it to _____! My best _____ from
                        A PLACE   NOUN

_____ class bought me a map of _____.
     LANGUAGE   FOREIGN COUNTRY

I can't wait to hang it in the _____! But my very
                                     ROOM

favorite _____ is the new _____ my
              NOUN   VEHICLE

uncle _____ gave me. It's _____ and
        CELEBRITY (MALE)   COLOR

goes _____ mph!
          NUMBER

MAD LIBS® is fun to play with friends, but you can also play it by yourself! To begin with, DO NOT look at the story on the page below. Fill in the blanks on this page with the words called for. Then, using the words you have selected, fill in the blank spaces in the story.

Now you've created your own hilarious MAD LIBS® game!

CLASS TRIP

SILLY WORD _____

A PLACE _____

VERB _____

COLOR _____

ARTICLE OF CLOTHING _____

PLURAL NOUN _____

NOUN _____

CELEBRITY (FEMALE) _____

VERB ENDING IN "ING" _____

VERB _____

ADJECTIVE _____

SAME SILLY WORD _____

NOUN _____

VERB (PAST TENSE) _____

SAME SILLY WORD _____

ADJECTIVE _____

SAME PLACE _____

PLURAL NOUN _____

VERB _____

VEHICLE (PLURAL) _____

ADJECTIVE _____

PLURAL NOUN _____

CLASS TRIP

For our final class trip our teacher Mr. _____ announced
                                        SILLY WORD

that we're going to _____! I'm so excited I can hardly
                     A PLACE

_____! I'm bringing my new _____
     VERB   COLOR

_____, my fancy _____, and of course
ARTICLE OF CLOTHING   PLURAL NOUN

my _____. My best friend _____ is
      NOUN   CELEBRITY (FEMALE)

_____ too, which will _____ the trip
VERB ENDING IN "ING"   VERB

even more _____. Mr. _____ said we can
            ADJECTIVE   SAME SILLY WORD

even share a/an _____! When I heard, I was so excited
                    NOUN

I _____! Mr. _____ said that while we're
  VERB (PAST TENSE)   SAME SILLY WORD

visiting the _____ village of _____ we can
                ADJECTIVE   SAME PLACE

do everything that the _____ do. We'll be able to
                          PLURAL NOUN

_____ in huge _____ and sleep in
     VERB   VEHICLE (PLURAL)

_____ _____.
   ADJECTIVE   PLURAL NOUN

MAD LIBS® is fun to play with friends, but you can also play it by yourself! To begin with, DO NOT look at the story on the page below. Fill in the blanks on this page with the words called for. Then, using the words you have selected, fill in the blank spaces in the story.

Now you've created your own hilarious MAD LIBS® game!

YOU'RE INVITED!

ADJECTIVE_____

VERB ENDING IN "ING" _____

TYPE OF FOOD (PLURAL) _____

TYPE OF LIQUID _____

ADJECTIVE_____

VERB _____

ARTICLE OF CLOTHING_____

ADJECTIVE_____

PART OF THE BODY (PLURAL) _____

VERB ENDING IN "ING" _____

PERSON IN ROOM (MALE)_____

VERB ENDING IN "ING" _____

SOMETHING ALIVE _____

PLURAL NOUN _____

CELEBRITY (FEMALE) _____

ARTICLE OF CLOTHING (PLURAL)_____

MAD LIBS

YOU'RE INVITED!

Here are some _____ tips for _____ the
               ADJECTIVE   VERB ENDING IN "ING"

best graduation party ever!

- Provide your guests with plenty of _____
                                         TYPE OF FOOD (PLURAL)

  and _____. No one likes to be hungry
         TYPE OF LIQUID

  or _____!
        ADJECTIVE

- _____ your fanciest _____
      VERB   ARTICLE OF CLOTHING

  and wear _____ shoes. You wouldn't want your
                ADJECTIVE

  _____ to hurt while you're
     PART OF THE BODY (PLURAL)

  _____ with _____.
   VERB ENDING IN "ING"   PERSON IN ROOM (MALE)

- When _____ at a party, it's always polite
          VERB ENDING IN "ING"

  to bring fresh _____ or a box of
                    SOMETHING ALIVE

  _____. At least that's what _____
     PLURAL NOUN   CELEBRITY (FEMALE)

  says you should do!

- Last but not least, you should always wear clean

  _____!
   ARTICLE OF CLOTHING (PLURAL)

From GRADUATION MAD LIBS® • Copyright © 2005 by Price Stern Sloan,
an imprint of Penguin Random House LLC, 345 Hudson Street, New York, NY 10014.

MAD LIBS® is fun to play with friends, but you can also play it by yourself! To begin with, DO NOT look at the story on the page below. Fill in the blanks on this page with the words called for. Then, using the words you have selected, fill in the blank spaces in the story.

Now you've created your own hilarious MAD LIBS® game!

FRIENDSHIPS

ADJECTIVE_____

ADJECTIVE_____

ADJECTIVE_____

PLURAL NOUN _____

ADJECTIVE_____

NOUN _____

PLURAL NOUN _____

LAST NAME OF PERSON IN ROOM _____

NOUN _____

PLURAL NOUN _____

CELEBRITY (MALE)_____

PLURAL NOUN _____

NOUN _____

NOUN _____

PERSON IN ROOM _____

NOUN _____

NOUN _____

NOUN _____

ADJECTIVE_____

PLURAL NOUN _____

NOUN

FRIENDSHIPS

One of the particularly _____ things about graduating is
                              ADJECTIVE

the _____ friendships that you make. There's a/an
       ADJECTIVE

_____ saying that the _____ that begin
ADJECTIVE   PLURAL NOUN

in _____ school often last a lifetime. A shining
      ADJECTIVE

_____ of this is my own father's relationship with three
   NOUN

_____. One of them, Ralph _____,
PLURAL NOUN   LAST NAME OF PERSON IN ROOM

is a fashion _____ who designs women's _____.
          NOUN   PLURAL NOUN

_____, who is six feet nine _____ tall, is a
CELEBRITY (MALE)   PLURAL NOUN

professional _____ player, and Dad's oldest _____ is
         NOUN   NOUN

_____, who sells cars and _____
PERSON IN ROOM   NOUN

insurance. They meet regularly at a coffee _____ in our
                                  NOUN

_____ and talk about _____ times. I hope my
   NOUN   ADJECTIVE

best _____ will be part of my _____ as long as
     PLURAL NOUN   NOUN

my dad's friends have been in his.

MAD LIBS® is fun to play with friends, but you can also play it by yourself! To begin with, DO NOT look at the story on the page below. Fill in the blanks on this page with the words called for. Then, using the words you have selected, fill in the blank spaces in the story.

Now you've created your own hilarious MAD LIBS® game!

CLASS PRESIDENT

PLURAL NOUN _____

VERB _____

PLURAL NOUN _____

YEAR _____

VERB (PAST TENSE)_____

NUMBER _____

LANGUAGE _____

PLURAL NOUN _____

FOREIGN COUNTRY _____

NUMBER _____

ADJECTIVE_____

SILLY WORD_____

NUMBER _____

ADJECTIVE_____

OCCUPATION (PLURAL) _____

ADJECTIVE_____

VERB ENDING IN "ING" _____

SAME YEAR_____

ADJECTIVE_____

MAD LIBS
CLASS PRESIDENT

Good morning, ladies and _____. As your class president,
_{PLURAL NOUN}

I'd like to _____ a few _____ about the
_{VERB} _{PLURAL NOUN}

graduating class of _____. We've all _____
_{YEAR} _{VERB (PAST TENSE)}

hard over the past _____ years and what a great time
_{NUMBER}

we've had! We've studied _____, learned about
_{LANGUAGE}

_____ in _____, and even learned how
_{PLURAL NOUN} _{FOREIGN COUNTRY}

to count to _____! That's pretty _____ if
_{NUMBER} _{ADJECTIVE}

you ask me. Especially since we had Mrs. _____ as our
_{SILLY WORD}

teacher for the past _____ years. She was one of the most
_{NUMBER}

_____ _____ we've ever had! I think
_{ADJECTIVE} _{OCCUPATION (PLURAL)}

this year's class is the most _____ ever. Although I'm
_{ADJECTIVE}

sad to be _____, I know the class of _____
_{VERB ENDING IN "ING"} _{SAME YEAR}

will do _____ things in the future.
_{ADJECTIVE}

MAD LIBS® is fun to play with friends, but you can also play it by yourself! To begin with, DO NOT look at the story on the page below. Fill in the blanks on this page with the words called for. Then, using the words you have selected, fill in the blank spaces in the story.

Now you've created your own hilarious MAD LIBS® game!

OUR YEARBOOK

ADJECTIVE _____

EXCLAMATION _____

VERB (PAST TENSE) _____

VERB (PAST TENSE) _____

ADJECTIVE _____

TYPE OF SPORT _____

SILLY WORD _____

LANGUAGE _____

PLURAL NOUN _____

NUMBER _____

PERSON IN ROOM (MALE) _____

PERSON IN ROOM (FEMALE) _____

OCCUPATION _____

ADJECTIVE _____

OCCUPATION (PLURAL) _____

VERB ENDING IN "ING" _____

PLURAL NOUN _____

VERB _____

PLURAL NOUN _____

PART OF THE BODY _____

MAD LIBS
OUR YEARBOOK

On the last day of school, our _____ yearbooks came

ADJECTIVE

out. Everyone yelled _____ and _____ to

EXCLAMATION   VERB (PAST TENSE)

grab one. When we _____ it, we couldn't believe how

VERB (PAST TENSE)

_____ it came out! It was filled with pictures of our

ADJECTIVE

_____ team the _____, the _____

TYPE OF SPORT   SILLY WORD   LANGUAGE

club, and our school marching band the _____. There

PLURAL NOUN

were _____ pages devoted to Homecoming, where

NUMBER

_____ and _____ were named king

PERSON IN ROOM (MALE)   PERSON IN ROOM (FEMALE)

and _____. There were even snapshots of our

OCCUPATION

_____ _____. After we finished

ADJECTIVE   OCCUPATION (PLURAL)

_____ through all of the cool _____,

VERB ENDING IN "ING"   PLURAL NOUN

everyone grabbed a pen so we could _____ one

VERB

another's books. I signed so many _____, I thought my

PLURAL NOUN

_____ would fall off!

PART OF THE BODY

From GRADUATION MAD LIBS® • Copyright © 2005 by Price Stern Sloan,
an imprint of Penguin Random House LLC, 345 Hudson Street, New York, NY 10014.

MAD LIBS® is fun to play with friends, but you can also play it by yourself! To begin with, DO NOT look at the story on the page below. Fill in the blanks on this page with the words called for. Then, using the words you have selected, fill in the blank spaces in the story.

Now you've created your own hilarious MAD LIBS® game!

WHEN I GROW UP

NUMBER _____

VERB ENDING IN "ING" _____

NOUN _____

LAST NAME OF PERSON IN ROOM_____

VERB ENDING IN "ING" _____

ADVERB_____

OCCUPATION _____

OCCUPATION _____

ADJECTIVE_____

NUMBER _____

A PLACE _____

PLURAL NOUN _____

NUMBER _____

NOUN _____

A PLACE _____

PLURAL NOUN _____

VEHICLE _____

ADJECTIVE_____

VERB ENDING IN "ING" _____

WHEN I GROW UP

Now that I've graduated from grade _____, I'm going to
                                          NUMBER

start _____ more often. After all, I'm practically
        VERB ENDING IN "ING"

a/an _____! Since I want to be just like Donald
              NOUN

_____ when I grow up, I'd better start
     LAST NAME OF PERSON IN ROOM

_____ as _____ as possible. I think this
  VERB ENDING IN "ING"   ADVERB

summer I'm going to get a part-time job as a/an _____ or
                                                    OCCUPATION

a/an _____. That will teach me how to be _____
         OCCUPATION   ADJECTIVE

and maybe I'll even make _____ dollars! Then I can put all
                              NUMBER

of my money in the _____ and collect _____.
                      A PLACE   PLURAL NOUN

When I retire at age _____, I'll be a/an _____.
                          NUMBER   NOUN

Maybe I'll even get to live on the beach in _____, buy
                                                A PLACE

expensive _____, and drive a fancy _____.
              PLURAL NOUN   VEHICLE

Wouldn't that be _____? I'd better start
                          ADJECTIVE

_____ right away!
  VERB ENDING IN "ING"

MAD LIBS® is fun to play with friends, but you can also play it by yourself! To begin with, DO NOT look at the story on the page below. Fill in the blanks on this page with the words called for. Then, using the words you have selected, fill in the blank spaces in the story.

Now you've created your own hilarious MAD LIBS® game!

THANK YOU

PLURAL NOUN _____

A PLACE _____

ADVERB _____

NOUN _____

VERB _____

NUMBER _____

LANGUAGE _____

ADJECTIVE _____

PLURAL NOUN _____

CELEBRITY (FEMALE) _____

VERB _____

PERSON IN ROOM (FEMALE) _____

CELEBRITY (MALE) _____

PART OF THE BODY _____

VERB ENDING IN "ING" _____

ROOM _____

VERB ENDING IN "ING" _____

A PLACE _____

NOUN _____

NOUN _____

SILLY WORD _____

NOUN _____

MAD LIBS
THANK YOU

There are so many _____ I want to thank for helping
                        PLURAL NOUN

me graduate from _____. First of all, I have to thank my
                        A PLACE

mom and dad. They've _____ helped me with my
                            ADVERB

_____, taught me how to _____ to
        NOUN   VERB

_____, and how to write in _____. They're
        NUMBER   LANGUAGE

the most _____ _____ ever! Next I'd like to
            ADJECTIVE   PLURAL NOUN

thank my teacher _____ for always showing me how to
                    CELEBRITY (FEMALE)

properly _____ my ABCs and 123s. Of course I have to thank
            VERB

my best friends, _____ and _____.
                    PERSON IN ROOM (FEMALE)   CELEBRITY (MALE)

I will always hold close to my _____ the times we spent
                                    PART OF THE BODY

_____ in my _____ and _____ in
VERB ENDING IN "ING"   ROOM   VERB ENDING IN "ING"

the _____. I would like to give a special thank-you to Mrs.
        A PLACE

_____, who taught me how to play the _____.
    NOUN   NOUN

And thank you, Mr. _____! Without you, I never would
                        SILLY WORD

have passed _____ class!
                NOUN

MAD LIBS® is fun to play with friends, but you can also play it by yourself! To begin with, DO NOT look at the story on the page below. Fill in the blanks on this page with the words called for. Then, using the words you have selected, fill in the blank spaces in the story.

Now you've created your own hilarious MAD LIBS® game!

TIPS FOR THE NEW GRAD

A PLACE _____

PLURAL NOUN _____

VERB _____

NOUN _____

NOUN _____

ADJECTIVE _____

CELEBRITY (MALE) _____

ARTICLE OF CLOTHING _____

ADJECTIVE _____

PLURAL NOUN _____

NOUN _____

OCCUPATION _____

NUMBER _____

NOUN _____

MAD LIBS

TIPS FOR THE NEW GRAD

Now that you've finally graduated from _____, you'll
                                        A PLACE
need some really good _____ to make sure you
                          PLURAL NOUN
_____ your way to the top! The following tips will help
      VERB
you become a huge _____:
                       NOUN

- Carry a/an _____ with you at all times. This
                   NOUN
  will make you look very _____. People
                              ADJECTIVE
  will think you look just like _____.
                                  CELEBRITY (MALE)

- Always wear a clean, pressed _____. After all,
                                  ARTICLE OF CLOTHING
  nobody will hire a/an _____ dresser!
                            ADJECTIVE

- It's a smart idea to have your own customized

  _____. That way, people will always
       PLURAL NOUN
  remember your name and phone _____.
                                    NOUN

- Be sure you visit the _____ at least
                            OCCUPATION
  _____ times a week. You wouldn't want
       NUMBER
  your _____ to look out of place!
            NOUN

From GRADUATION MAD LIBS® • Copyright © 2005 by Price Stern Sloan,
an imprint of Penguin Random House LLC, 345 Hudson Street, New York, NY 10014.

MAD LIBS® is fun to play with friends, but you can also play it by yourself! To begin with, DO NOT look at the story on the page below. Fill in the blanks on this page with the words called for. Then, using the words you have selected, fill in the blank spaces in the story.

Now you've created your own hilarious MAD LIBS® game!

FINAL FAREWELL

A PLACE _____

ADJECTIVE _____

OCCUPATION (PLURAL) _____

PLURAL NOUN _____

NOUN _____

PLURAL NOUN _____

SILLY WORD _____

TYPE OF FOOD _____

TYPE OF FOOD _____

NOUN _____

PERSON IN ROOM (FEMALE) _____

NOUN _____

PERSON IN ROOM (MALE) _____

NOUN _____

ADVERB _____

SILLY WORD _____

ADJECTIVE _____

VERB (PAST TENSE) _____

PART OF THE BODY _____

VERB ENDING IN "ING" _____

MAD LIBS

FINAL FAREWELL

My last day at _____ was extremely _____.
　　　　　　　　　　　 A PLACE　　　　　　　　　　　　　　　ADJECTIVE

First, our _____ told us how proud they were that
　　　　　 OCCUPATION (PLURAL)

we turned into such great _____. Then we had a/an
　　　　　　　　　　　　　　　　 PLURAL NOUN

_____ where all of our family and _____
　　　 NOUN　　　　　　　　　　　　　　　　　　　　　 PLURAL NOUN

came to bid us farewell. Mrs. _____ surprised us with a
　　　　　　　　　　　　　　　 SILLY WORD

big _____ with _____ frosting! I thought it
　　 TYPE OF FOOD　　　　　　　 TYPE OF FOOD

tasted like a/an _____, but my friend _____
　　　　　　　　　 NOUN　　　　　　　　　　　 PERSON IN ROOM (FEMALE)

thought it was the best piece of _____ she ever had!
　　　　　　　　　　　　　　　　　　 NOUN

Then Mr. _____ announced that he had a big
　　　　　 PERSON IN ROOM (MALE)

_____ for us! _____, my favorite band
　　 NOUN　　　　　　　　　　　 ADVERB

_____ arrived! They were _____! They
　 SILLY WORD　　　　　　　　　　　　　　　　 ADJECTIVE

_____ all of my favorite songs like "Rock Your
　 VERB (PAST TENSE)

_____" and "We're _____"! This was
 PART OF THE BODY　　　　　　　　　 VERB ENDING IN "ING"

the coolest graduation ever!

From GRADUATION MAD LIBS® • Copyright © 2005 by Price Stern Sloan,
an imprint of Penguin Random House LLC, 345 Hudson Street, New York, NY 10014.

MAD LIBS® is fun to play with friends, but you can also play it by yourself! To begin with, DO NOT look at the story on the page below. Fill in the blanks on this page with the words called for. Then, using the words you have selected, fill in the blank spaces in the story.

Now you've created your own hilarious MAD LIBS® game!

MY FIRST GRADUATION

NUMBER _____

PART OF THE BODY _____

ADJECTIVE _____

PLURAL NOUN _____

ADJECTIVE _____

VERB _____

PLURAL NOUN _____

NOUN _____

PLURAL NOUN _____

PLURAL NOUN _____

LIQUID _____

ADJECTIVE _____

NOUN _____

NOUN _____

NOUN _____

ADJECTIVE _____

NOUN _____

NOUN _____

MAD LIBS

MY FIRST GRADUATION

Even though _____ years have gone by, my kindergarten
              NUMBER

graduation is still fresh in my _____. I have _____
                   PART OF THE BODY   ADJECTIVE

memories of my very first day. I remember walking into the room

with my _____ shaking. Fortunately, the teacher was very
       PLURAL NOUN

_____ and made me _____. In no time at all, I
ADJECTIVE   VERB

learned how to count _____, write my own full
                  PLURAL NOUN

_____, and color _____. Every day, we had snack
NOUN   PLURAL NOUN

time. Some of us ate cheese and _____, others had cookies
                PLURAL NOUN

and _____. The rest of the day, the teacher read a/an
   LIQUID

_____ _____ to us, like *Charlie and the*
ADJECTIVE   NOUN

_____ *Factory*. All of my days in kindergarten are etched
NOUN

in my _____. I really hated to leave. Actually, I didn't
      NOUN

graduate! The nurse sent me home that day because I had a/an

_____ cold and a hacking _____. The school
ADJECTIVE   NOUN

eventually mailed my _____ to me.
            NOUN

From GRADUATION MAD LIBS® • Copyright © 2005 by Price Stern Sloan,
an imprint of Penguin Random House LLC, 345 Hudson Street, New York, NY 10014.

MAD LIBS® is fun to play with friends, but you can also play it by yourself! To begin with, DO NOT look at the story on the page below. Fill in the blanks on this page with the words called for. Then, using the words you have selected, fill in the blank spaces in the story.

Now you've created your own hilarious MAD LIBS® game!

MOST LIKELY TO...

NUMBER _____

VERB _____

PERSON IN ROOM (FEMALE)_____

VERB _____

A PLACE _____

NOUN _____

SILLY WORD_____

ADJECTIVE_____

VERB _____

PERSON IN ROOM (FEMALE)_____

A PLACE _____

NUMBER _____

LANGUAGE _____

SILLY WORD_____

OCCUPATION _____

VERB _____

VERB _____

ADJECTIVE_____

A PLACE _____

VERB ENDING IN "ING" _____

PLURAL NOUN _____

MAD LIBS

MOST LIKELY TO . . .

_____ pages of our yearbook were dedicated to "The Person
<small>NUMBER</small>

Most Likely To . . ." when we _____ up. My best friend,
<small>VERB</small>

_____, was voted most likely to _____
<small>PERSON IN ROOM (FEMALE)</small> <small>VERB</small>

in _____, because she wants to be a movie _____
<small>A PLACE</small> <small>NOUN</small>

when she grows up. Peter _____ was voted most
<small>SILLY WORD</small>

_____, because all the girls in my class _____
<small>ADJECTIVE</small> <small>VERB</small>

when he walks by. _____ was voted most likely
<small>PERSON IN ROOM (FEMALE)</small>

to graduate from _____ with honors, because she got
<small>A PLACE</small>

a/an _____ on every _____ test last
<small>NUMBER</small> <small>LANGUAGE</small>

semester. My friend _____ got everyone's vote for the
<small>SILLY WORD</small>

girl most likely to be a/an _____, because she loves to
<small>OCCUPATION</small>

make people _____. And me? I was named the most likely
<small>VERB</small>

to _____, because of all of my _____
<small>VERB</small> <small>ADJECTIVE</small>

adventures traveling to _____ and _____
<small>A PLACE</small> <small>VERB ENDING IN "ING"</small>

through the Rocky _____.
<small>PLURAL NOUN</small>

MAD LIBS® is fun to play with friends, but you can also play it by yourself! To begin with, DO NOT look at the story on the page below. Fill in the blanks on this page with the words called for. Then, using the words you have selected, fill in the blank spaces in the story.

Now you've created your own hilarious MAD LIBS® game!

MEMORIES

ADJECTIVE _____

ADJECTIVE _____

ADJECTIVE _____

ADJECTIVE _____

PLURAL NOUN _____

VERB ENDING IN "ING" _____

PLURAL NOUN _____

VERB ENDING IN "ING" _____

PLURAL NOUN _____

NOUN _____

ADJECTIVE _____

NOUN _____

ADJECTIVE _____

PLURAL NOUN _____

PLURAL NOUN _____

PLURAL NOUN _____

ADJECTIVE _____

PLURAL NOUN _____

MAD LIBS®
MEMORIES

Some of the _____ memories I have of _____
                    ADJECTIVE   ADJECTIVE

school concern the _____ trips we took to so many
                        ADJECTIVE

_____ places. I'll always remember a visit to the zoo where
   ADJECTIVE

we saw the wild _____ _____ in their cages
                  PLURAL NOUN   VERB ENDING IN "ING"

and the flying _____ practically _____ in
                 PLURAL NOUN   VERB ENDING IN "ING"

everyone's hair. There were also the wonderful science

_____ at the _____ museum and the trips to a/an
   PLURAL NOUN   NOUN

_____ theater where we saw *The Lion* _____ and
   ADJECTIVE   NOUN

The _____ *Mermaid.* These are the kinds of _____
         ADJECTIVE   PLURAL NOUN

that will last forever. I'm sure I'll be telling my own _____
                                                          PLURAL NOUN

about them in _____ to come and, hopefully, they'll be
                  PLURAL NOUN

visiting _____ places and creating _____ of
             ADJECTIVE   PLURAL NOUN

their own.

From GRADUATION MAD LIBS® • Copyright © 2005 by Price Stern Sloan,
an imprint of Penguin Random House LLC, 345 Hudson Street, New York, NY 10014.

MAD LIBS® is fun to play with friends, but you can also play it by yourself! To begin with, DO NOT look at the story on the page below. Fill in the blanks on this page with the words called for. Then, using the words you have selected, fill in the blank spaces in the story.

Now you've created your own hilarious MAD LIBS® game!

MY DIPLOMA

ADJECTIVE_____

ADJECTIVE_____

COLOR_____

PLURAL NOUN _____

ADJECTIVE_____

SILLY WORD_____

NOUN _____

VERB _____

EXCLAMATION_____

VERB (PAST TENSE)_____

ADJECTIVE_____

VERB ENDING IN "ING" _____

VERB _____

ADJECTIVE_____

PERSON IN ROOM (MALE)_____

VERB _____

ADVERB_____

COLOR_____

VERB _____

ADVERB_____

NOUN _____

ROOM _____

MAD LIBS®
MY DIPLOMA

I can't believe I got my _____ diploma! It's
                        ADJECTIVE

_____! It is _____ and lists all of the
   ADJECTIVE   COLOR

_____ I took during _____ school.
  PLURAL NOUN   ADJECTIVE

When Principal _____ called my _____
                SILLY WORD   NOUN

to _____ up and get it, I was so excited I yelled
    VERB

_____! I practically _____ it out of his hand!
 EXCLAMATION   VERB (PAST TENSE)

My parents were so _____ to see me _____
               ADJECTIVE   VERB ENDING IN "ING"

my diploma that they actually started to _____! My
                                VERB

_____ little brother _____ started to
  ADJECTIVE   PERSON IN ROOM (MALE)

_____ so _____ that my mom's face turned
   VERB   ADVERB

bright _____, which made her _____ even
      COLOR   VERB

more. When I got home, I _____ put my diploma in a/an
                  ADVERB

_____ and hung it up in the _____.
  NOUN   ROOM

From GRADUATION MAD LIBS® • Copyright © 2005 by Price Stern Sloan,
an imprint of Penguin Random House LLC, 345 Hudson Street, New York, NY 10014.

MAD LIBS® is fun to play with friends, but you can also play it by yourself! To begin with, DO NOT look at the story on the page below. Fill in the blanks on this page with the words called for. Then, using the words you have selected, fill in the blank spaces in the story.

Now you've created your own hilarious MAD LIBS® game!

MY TEACHERS

PLURAL NOUN _____

A PLACE _____

ADJECTIVE_____

SILLY WORD_____

VERB _____

NOUN _____

NUMBER _____

PERSON IN ROOM (FEMALE)_____

TYPE OF FOOD (PLURAL) _____

LANGUAGE _____

CELEBRITY (MALE)_____

OCCUPATION (PLURAL) _____

NOUN _____

PLURAL NOUN _____

VERB _____

PLURAL NOUN _____

ADJECTIVE_____

ADVERB_____

LAST NAME OF PERSON _____

NUMBER _____

NOUN _____

ADVERB_____

SAME LAST NAME OF PERSON_____

MAD LIBS
MY TEACHERS

One of the _____ I will miss most about graduating
               PLURAL NOUN

from _____ is all of the _____ teachers
      A PLACE   ADJECTIVE

that I had. There is Mr. _____, who taught me how to
                     SILLY WORD

_____ the _____ and count to _____.
VERB   NOUN   NUMBER

Then there is Mrs. _____, who always brought
          PERSON IN ROOM (FEMALE)

_____ to _____ class. And _____
TYPE OF FOOD (PLURAL)   LANGUAGE   CELEBRITY (MALE)

is one of my favorite _____ ever! He was the school's
              OCCUPATION (PLURAL)

drama _____, and he put on the best _____ ever!
      NOUN   PLURAL NOUN

He let me _____ the lead in the school play *Guys and*
         VERB

_____. But I think out of all my _____ teachers,
PLURAL NOUN   ADJECTIVE

the one I will miss _____ is Mrs. _____.
          ADVERB   LAST NAME OF PERSON

She always gave me a/an _____ on _____ tests and
              NUMBER   NOUN

would _____ help me with my homework. I'll miss you,
      ADVERB

Mrs. _____!
    SAME LAST NAME OF PERSON

From GRADUATION MAD LIBS® • Copyright © 2005 by Price Stern Sloan,
of Penguin Random House LLC, 345 Hudson Street, New York, NY 10014.

MAD LIBS® is fun to play with friends, but you can also play it by yourself! To begin with, DO NOT look at the story on the page below. Fill in the blanks on this page with the words called for. Then, using the words you have selected, fill in the blank spaces in the story.

Now you've created your own hilarious MAD LIBS® game!

THE FAREWELL DANCE

ADJECTIVE_____

PLURAL NOUN _____

PLURAL NOUN _____

ADJECTIVE_____

NOUN _____

ADJECTIVE_____

ADJECTIVE_____

PLURAL NOUN _____

NOUN _____

ADVERB_____

ADJECTIVE_____

PLURAL NOUN _____

PLURAL NOUN _____

NOUN _____

PLURAL NOUN _____

NOUN _____

MAD LIBS
THE FAREWELL DANCE

A farewell dance is both a happy and a/an _____
ADJECTIVE

occasion. It may be the last time you see many of your

_____ with whom you've spent the most important
PLURAL NOUN

_____ of your life. This year our _____
PLURAL NOUN   ADJECTIVE

dance will be held in the school _____. It will be
NOUN

decorated in a very _____ fashion. On the walls will
ADJECTIVE

be caricatures of our _____ teachers. Helium
ADJECTIVE

_____ will be floating overhead, and a revolving crystal
PLURAL NOUN

_____ will _____ reflect light on the
NOUN   ADVERB

_____ floor. Most of the boys will be wearing rented
ADJECTIVE

_____ and most of the girls will be dressed in formal
PLURAL NOUN

_____. And here's the big surprise: We have enough
PLURAL NOUN

_____ in our budget to book the Beastie
NOUN

_____ to supply the music! All in all, it promises to be
PLURAL NOUN

a/an _____ to remember.
NOUN

MAD LIBS® is fun to play with friends, but you can also play it by yourself! To begin with, DO NOT look at the story on the page below. Fill in the blanks on this page with the words called for. Then, using the words you have selected, fill in the blank spaces in the story.

Now you've created your own hilarious MAD LIBS® game!

SAYING GOOD-BYE

VERB ENDING IN "ING" _____

PLURAL NOUN _____

VERB _____

CELEBRITY (MALE) _____

NUMBER _____

ADJECTIVE _____

PERSON IN ROOM (FEMALE) _____

TYPE OF SPORT _____

SILLY WORD _____

PLURAL NOUN _____

VERB _____

ADJECTIVE _____

PLURAL NOUN _____

NOUN _____

CELEBRITY (FEMALE) _____

ADVERB _____

TOWN _____

VERB _____

MAD LIBS®
SAYING GOOD-BYE

One of the hardest things about _____ from school
_{VERB ENDING IN "ING"}

is saying good-bye to all of my good _____. I'm going to
_{PLURAL NOUN}

_____ them so much! How can I say farewell to my best
_{VERB}

friend, _____? We've gone to school together since
_{CELEBRITY (MALE)}

I was _____ years old! Then there is my _____
_{NUMBER} _{ADJECTIVE}

friend _____, who was on my _____
_{PERSON IN ROOM (FEMALE)} _{TYPE OF SPORT}

team. I'll hate to say _____ to her! Then there's the
_{SILLY WORD}

group of _____ that I used to _____ with—they
_{PLURAL NOUN} _{VERB}

are the most _____ _____ ever! I'll
_{ADJECTIVE} _{PLURAL NOUN}

miss my _____ friend _____ most
_{NOUN} _{CELEBRITY (FEMALE)}

_____. But she lives in _____ so I'll get to
_{ADVERB} _{TOWN}

_____ her all the time.
_{VERB}

From GRADUATION MAD LIBS® • Copyright © 2005 by Price Stern Sloan,
an imprint of Penguin Random House LLC, 345 Hudson Street, New York, NY 10014.

MAD LIBS® is fun to play with friends, but you can also play it by yourself! To begin with, DO NOT look at the story on the page below. Fill in the blanks on this page with the words called for. Then, using the words you have selected, fill in the blank spaces in the story.

Now you've created your own hilarious MAD LIBS® game!

NEW SCHOOL JITTERS

VERB ENDING IN "ING" _____

NUMBER _____

ADJECTIVE _____

TOWN _____

PLURAL NOUN _____

VEHICLE _____

ADJECTIVE _____

ADJECTIVE _____

PLURAL NOUN _____

VERB ENDING IN "ING" _____

A PLACE _____

TYPE OF SPORT _____

CELEBRITY (MALE) _____

OCCUPATION _____

EXCLAMATION _____

MAD LIBS®
NEW SCHOOL JITTERS

Even though I'm not _____ to my new school for

                 VERB ENDING IN "ING"

another _____ months, I'm already getting _____

          NUMBER   ADJECTIVE

about it. It's all the way in _____, which is far away from

                                    TOWN

all of my neighborhood _____. Because it's so far away,

                           PLURAL NOUN

I'll have to take a/an _____ to school. Isn't that

                          VEHICLE

_____? But even though there are many _____

   ADJECTIVE   ADJECTIVE

things about starting a new school, there are also lots of things to be

excited about. I can't wait to make new _____, take

                                   PLURAL NOUN

exciting classes like _____, have lunch in the

                  VERB ENDING IN "ING"

_____, and join the _____ team. Plus, I

   A PLACE   TYPE OF SPORT

heard that _____ is a/an _____ there!

          CELEBRITY (MALE)   OCCUPATION

_____! I can't wait for school to start!

   EXCLAMATION

MAD LIBS® is fun to play with friends, but you can also play it by yourself! To begin with, DO NOT look at the story on the page below. Fill in the blanks on this page with the words called for. Then, using the words you have selected, fill in the blank spaces in the story.

Now you've created your own hilarious MAD LIBS® game!

CLASS RING

VERB ENDING IN "ING" _____

FOREIGN COUNTRY _____

ADJECTIVE_____

COLOR_____

COLOR_____

COLOR_____

PART OF THE BODY (PLURAL) _____

PERSON IN ROOM (FEMALE)_____

COLOR_____

TYPE OF FOOD _____

CELEBRITY (FEMALE) _____

CELEBRITY (MALE) _____

ADJECTIVE_____

PLURAL NOUN _____

YEAR _____

VERB _____

VERB _____

VERB _____

ROOM _____

ADJECTIVE_____

VERB _____

ADJECTIVE_____

PART OF THE BODY (PLURAL) _____

Today we're _____ our class rings! They came all the
     VERB ENDING IN "ING"

way from _____ and are _____ colors like
     FOREIGN COUNTRY   ADJECTIVE

_____ and _____. My ring is bright _____
COLOR   COLOR   COLOR

and matches my _____ perfectly. My best
     PART OF THE BODY (PLURAL)

friend _____ picked a/an _____ ring
     PERSON IN ROOM (FEMALE)   COLOR

the color of _____. She said it reminds her of the ring
     TYPE OF FOOD

that _____ got from _____, even though it's
     CELEBRITY (FEMALE)   CELEBRITY (MALE)

not as _____. And guess what? The ring even has our very
     ADJECTIVE

own _____ on it and says the "Class of _____"!
     PLURAL NOUN   YEAR

I know I'll _____ my class ring for as long as I _____.
     VERB   VERB

I am going to _____ it every day and keep it safe in my
     VERB

_____. That way my _____ little brother
ROOM   ADJECTIVE

won't be able to _____ his _____ little
     VERB   ADJECTIVE

_____ on it!
PART OF THE BODY (PLURAL)